D1555714

1001

KNIGHTS

VOL III   WISDOM

With Foreword by Richie Pope

DISCARDED

BY

BERTHOUD COMMUNITY
LIBRARY DISTRICT

THE GREAT WINDMILL

DISCARDED
BY
BERTHOUD COMMUNITY LIBRARY DISTRICT

1001 Knights: Volume III: Wisdom is a work of fiction. Names, characters, businesses, places, events, incidents, dragons, castles, & swords are either the products of the author's imagination or used in a fictitious manner. Any resemblance to actual persons, dragons, or knights, living or dead, or actual events is purely coincidental.

1001 Knights Curated by Annie Stoll & Kevin Jay Stanton
Art Direction & Design by Annie Stoll
Cover Illustration & Crest by Kevin Jay Stanton

1001 Knights is a 3 volume people-positive anthology.
There are over 260 artists who participated in *1001 Knights*.
The book in your hands is Vol. III, Wisdom.

1001 Knights: Volume III: Wisdom Copyright © 2017 by The Great Windmill / 1001 Knights
All art within this book Copyright © 2017 their respective artists.

All rights reserved. This book or any portion thereof may not be reproduced or used in any manner whatsoever without the express written permission of the publisher except for the use of brief quotations in a book review or for educational purposes in classrooms and libraries. All rights for individual art, stories, and media within this anthology belong to their creators. No part of this book may be reproduced or transmitted in any form or by any means, electronic or mechanical, including photography, xerography, and video recording, without the express written permission from the publisher, The Great Windmill.

1001 Knights was made possible by our generous Kickstarter backers.
Please visit our website to view a full list of their names at
www.OneThousandAndOneKnights.com/thankyou

Thank you to all the amazing artists. We hope that you, dear reader, check each of them out in the index & discover new and amazing worlds of art. Special thank you to the team who helped us created 1001 Knights: George Rohac & the Breadpig team, T.H., Shariq Ansari, Matt Pichette, Lillian Skye, & all our friends and family for believing in all of us and helping us make this project a reality.

Typefaces:
DropCaps are Ivory by Facetype Foundry. Ivory is inspired by a beautiful typeface used in an illustrated compendium about pomology from 1882. Body copy is Begum by Indian Type Foundry. The complete Begum super family was designed in India by Manushi Parikh. Logotype is based on Charcuterie Block a typeface created by Laura Worthington. Charcuterie is an homage to the inventiveness, passion, and care of peasants who proudly handed down recipes through generations.

First Printing, 2017

ISBN 978-0-9988204-2-2

www.OneThousandAndOneKnights.com | OneThousandAndOneKnights@gmail.com

"...Let us pick up our books and our pens. They are our most powerful weapons. One child, one teacher, one book and one pen can change the world."

—MALALA YOUSAFZAI,
TO THE UNITED NATIONS ON JULY 12, 2013

1001 KNIGHTS is a people-positive project that started out as a small zine and grew into so much more. Years in the making, there are more than 260 artists and over 3,000 Kickstarter backers who made this book possible. When 1001 Knights was first conceived, we vowed that all artists were welcome regardless of gender, sexual identity, race, creed, or nationality.

The only question posed was "What does it mean to be a knight?" And we will let you, dear reader, enjoy and be inspired by the incredible imagination of the artists of 1001 Knights...

TABLE OF CONTENTS

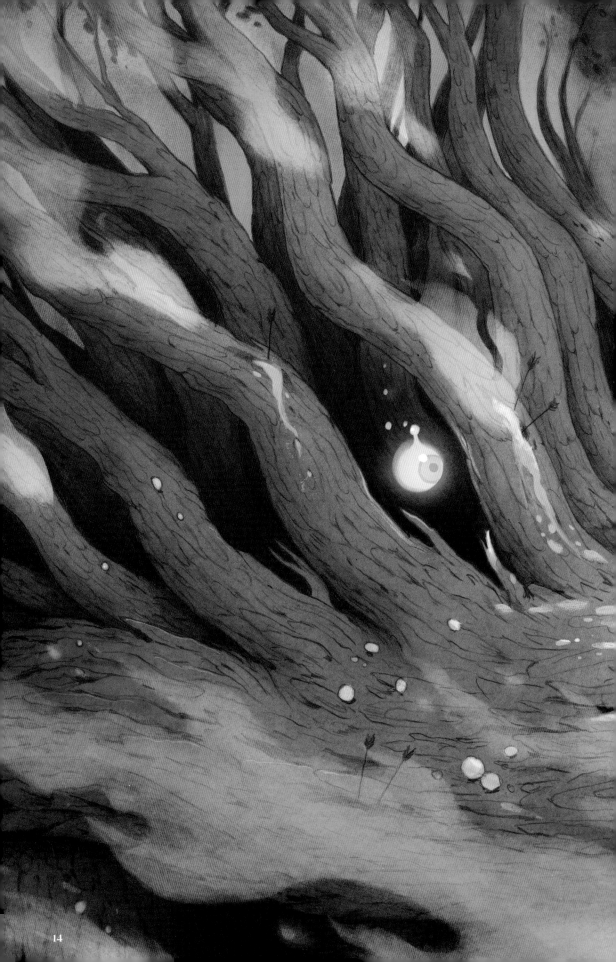

INTO THE WYLD QUEST

WORDS JONATHAN YING
PICTURES VICTORIA YING

22

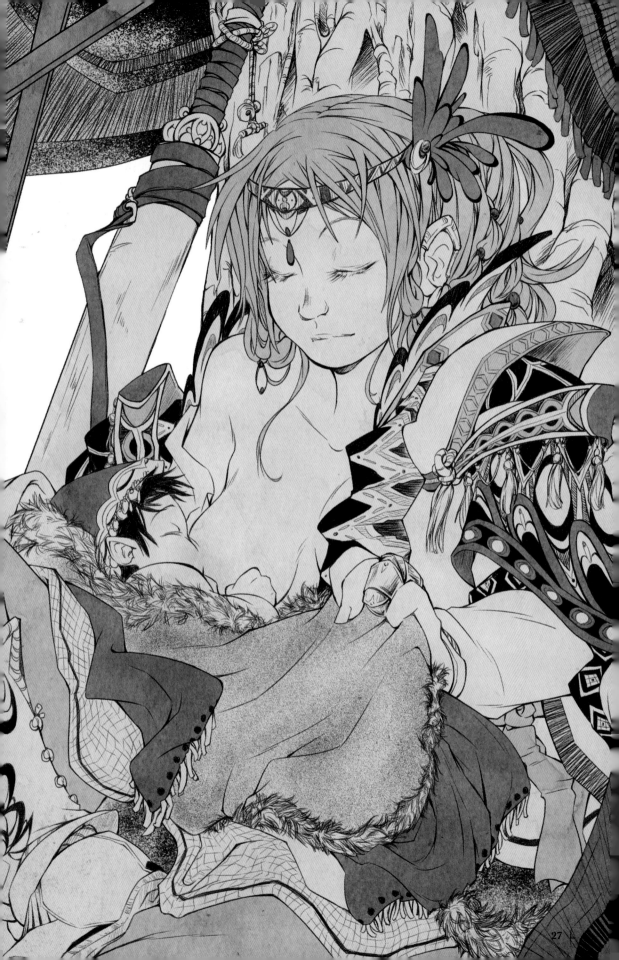

The Sky Knights
by Heidi Black

MORNING DRILL TIME, LADIES! SQUAD A ON AIR DRILLS, B ON YARD PRACTICE, C IS COOKING DUTY!

I never felt useful before

You were the smart one, but after mom and dad died...

That was before I learned I could fly

WHAT IS THE MEANING OF THIS, CAPTAIN? THIS IS INSUBORDINATION! A DIRECT VIOLATION OF ORDERS!

ALL OF THESE GIRLS, OUT HERE IN THE WILDS, ANSWERING TO NO MAN?

IF YOU THINK YOU CAN STOP ANY OF THEM, BE MY GUEST.

BUT MY GUESS? SHE'S PROBABLY HEADED TO SEE THE EMPEROR RIGHT NOW.

THIS IS RESTRICTED AIRSPACE. PLEASE STATE YOUR NAME AND RANK

I AM A MEMBER OF THE NORTH MOUNTAIN OUTPOST, UNDER CAPTAIN SELHAM.

I NEED TO SPEAK TO THE EMPEROR, URGENTLY.

WE CANNOT ALLOW YOU ANY CLOSER TO THE PALACE. ALTER YOUR COURSE IMMEDIATELY.

SORRY NOT HAPPENING, BOYS.

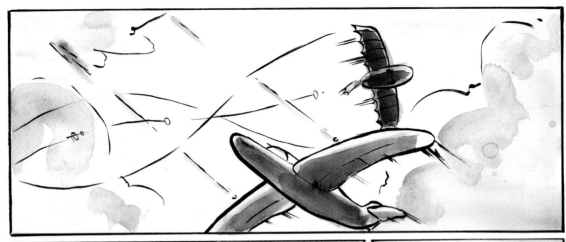

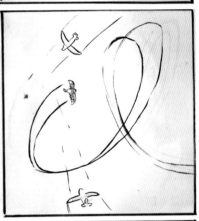

YOU'RE . . .

A WOMAN?

YES.

HEARING YOUR STORY... I APOLOGIZE.

MY GENERALS RARELY SPEAK OF THE WOMEN WHO FIGHT FOR ME. I HAD ASSUMED THEY TREATED YOU WELL.

PERHAPS THIS IS MY FAULT MORE THAN ANYONE'S.

MY FATHER RAISED ME JUST AS WELL AS MY BROTHER, BUT WHEN THEY BOTH DIED, EVERYTHING CHANGED.

EVERYONE SAYS THE PRINCESS - YOU - DIED.

THAT IS THE STORY THE COUNCIL TOLD THE COUNTRY.

THE COUNCIL SAW THE PERFECT OPPORTUNITY TO MAKE A PUPPET EMPEROR.

AND I TRUSTED THEM, BECAUSE THEY HAD BEEN LOYAL TO MY FATHER.

PERHAPS IT IS TIME I TRULY BEGAN TO RULE THIS COUNTRY.

I THOUGHT I WAS POWERLESS, BUT SEEING YOU FLY...

I DON'T UNDERSTAND

Dearest sister —
Everyone has settled into life at the palace well.

the captain is now in charge of training the palace guards.

Apparently it's hilarious to watch them try to do our drills.

And as for HER....
well...

Perhaps things are changing more than we ever dreamed.

The Sky Knights. End

LOOK AT YOU, YOU PATHETIC CREATURE.

HOW DARE YOU DEFY ME!

WHO ARE YOU TO ME, THE GREAT DRAGON OF THE DEEP?

YOU COULD NEVER REDEEM YOURSELF THIS WAY.

YOU ARE A SMALL AND BROKEN THING.

YOU DON'T EVEN GET IT DO YOU?

YOUR FAULT IS THAT YOU MISJUDGE ANYTHING...

...THAT IS PHYSICALLY SMALLER THAN YOU

CONSIDER YOUR OPPONENTS STRENGTH RATHER THAN HER SIZE!

BUT IT LOOKS LIKE MAYBE IT DOESN'T MATTER ANYMORE. EHH?

GOD, WORMS CAN BE SUCH - -

YES, I SEE SISTER. HER PERSEVERANCE DOES NOT DISAPPOINT.

INDEED SISTER. NOW TO SEE WHAT SHE DOES NEXT.

Lizzie
Parberry

45

THERE ARE REPORTS OF A MAGIC-USER CREATING MONSTERS IN THIS AREA. MOST OF THE RESIDENTS HAVE FLED.

Little Monsters
by Vanessa Satone

SCREE

WELL HELLO THERE LADIES!

...

WHAT BRINGS SOLDIERS TO THIS NEIGHBORHOOD? HAVEN'T YOU HEARD IT'S DANGEROUS HERE?

WE'RE HERE ON OFFICIAL MILITARY BUSINESS. NO NEED FOR YOU TO INTERFERE.

TWANG

GRRRRRRR

GRRR~

WHERE ARE THESE THINGS COMING FROM?

DASH!

AAAAAAA

49

DID YOU MAKE THESE CREATURES?

SO WHAT IF I DID?

HMMM...

WE'VE GOT NO CHOICE BUT TO BRING HER IN.

...

I'M NOT LETTING YOU ARREST HER.

SHE'S TERRORIZING PEOPLE WITH THESE MONSTERS.

WAK

SHE'S JUST A KID.

DO YOU REALLY THINK SENDING A YOUNG GIRL TO PRISON IS A NOBLE THING TO DO?

I GUESS SHE HAS A GOOD POINT.

I'M LETTING YOU OFF WITH A WARNING, BUT I'D LAY OFF MAKING MAGICAL HELLBEASTS FROM NOW ON.

Y...YES MA'AM.

I CAN'T BELIEVE YOU'D USE MY SENSE OF JUSTICE AGAINST ME LIKE THAT.

ISN'T THAT WHAT BEING A VALIANT KNIGHT IS ALL ABOUT?

OH NO.

KRAAN!

IT'S HER AGAIN.

SHE'S...

SO COOL.

ALEX ECKMAN-LAWN

I'M JUST... GONNA HANG BACK HERE. FOR A MINUTE.

SHE'S REALLY ON TOP OF HER SHIT.

· · ·

PLUS MY OUTFIT TODAY IS STUPID!

OWF!

OH! HEY...

HI...UM NICE SWORD. IS IT MYTHRIL?

OH THANKS! IT WAS MY DAD'S...

YEAH, IT SUCKS. I LIKE YOUR JACKET!

ALEX ECKMAN-LAWN

LAMPLIGHTER

Illustrated by: Mikey A. Grant
Cover and written by: S.M. Vidaurri

THANKS BUT, I ONLY I STOPPED THEM FROM STEALING THE CANDLE UP BY THE PURCHASE, YOU JUST HAPPENED TO GET FREE IN THE FIGHT.

FAIR ENOUGH – BUT IN THE END YOU CAME ALONG, AND I GOT OUT. DOSN'T REALLY MATTER MUCH AFTER THAT, DOES IT?

I AIN'T SAVING YOUR LIFE, NEITHER, JUST TELLING YOU SOMETHING YOU'D LIKE TO KNOW.

WELL, I APPRECIATE IT. THE LAMP ON DEATH'S HILL IS IMPORTANT, IT KEEPS BACK MOST OF THE– OH!

I'VE GOT TO BE GOING, LOVE.

LAMPLIGHTER.
THOUGHT YOU'D COME.

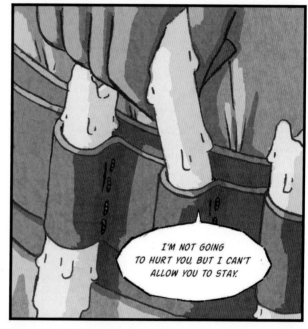

ON THE BRINK OF PUNISHMENT
BY MEGAN L. HEATON

s the last rays of sunlight faded from the horizon, Cotota counted beneath her breath. To the uneducated, and there was quite a few of them in the camp, it almost seemed like she was singing.

Cotota preferred to think of it as praying.

Thirty ... Twenty nine ... Twenty eight ...

"He's not here, aunt." She barely flinched as the foul alcohol-scented spittle from her eldest nephew landed on the back of her neck as she knelt upon the elaborate cushions that made up the imperial throne. "You promised me your son would be seen upon the horizon by sundown so we can begin the *kurultai*, and where is he? Can you not do anything right?"

Twenty five ... twenty four ... twenty three ... Why did men always have to smell like they spent their days drinking the sweet wines that dulled their senses and their wits? It was a timeless trope that was so very tiring. "He has been delayed, and you speak with impudence."

"You're the one who's impudent." Cotota stared hard into the eyes of her nephew Geser as he shifted around to loom over her. Geser was the eldest son of her deceased brother-in-law and the one who demanded that it was his right to run their tribe next. They followed the ways of the ancient ones on Earth, the ones once ruled by the great lord Genghis Khan. It was for that reason alone, to emulate the golden empire he once commanded, that Geser hadn't stolen the khanate by force. Not even he would go against the ways of Genghis.

Cotota, however, knew her history in a way the younger generation did not. Once again, the stories of the great wars of the power struggles following the dead of Genghis' son, Ögedai, raced through her head like they did every night when she tried to sleep. Like they did every day as she worked to rebuild what her husband had torn apart in the name of the great khans and their thirst for endless war. And with every breath, she hoped her eldest son, Dogar, would avoid the imperial city as long as possible.

Twenty one ... twenty ... nineteen ...

"Useless woman," Geser spat and reached for Cotota's robes. With a snarl and a flash, she unsheathed the knife she kept tucked in a wrist sheath and plunged it into Geser's thigh. He howled and toppled back as she calmly rose to her feet.

"Do something with that," she calmly informed the soldiers that rushed into her tent at Geser's cries. "He's had a slight mishap with his knife." She swept past them, ignoring Geser's cursing as she stood just outside the tent. The last rays of suns kissed the wind-swept fields, gleamed off the small tents that dotted the wide, flat terrain. She once heard the Earth steppes were wide and flat and so very green when the weather was good. She wasn't even quite sure what the color green was like. Such a concept didn't exist on her world. Even if it did, she didn't think she would care for it. Nothing could surpass the azure grasses and lilac skies that was her home. She was one with the steppes.

Nine ... eight ... seven ...

"Are you praying for your son's safety, my lady?" the soldier at her shoulder murmured.

Three ... two ... one ...

Cotota started to walk away from the imperial tents. "I will spend this evening with my ladies. Please make sure we are not disturbed. We will be working on our weaving."

"As you desire."

She weaved through the tents sedately, smiling at the children playing in the small square and the shopkeepers securing their wares for the night. Every few steps, someone rushed up to her with some sort of issue that her husband had always found tedious compared with the rush of going to war. He thought of the people they conquered as little more than cattle, and it was rumored that he was even considering allying with the great kingdoms to the south so he could take to space and expand the empire even further. It made Cotota's blood run cold.

After a half hour of being the leader that her husband never was, she arrived at one of the largest tents in the camp. Inside was said to house a hundred looms, as the highborn women of the tribe spent their evenings weaving. It was a task so sacred that not even Geser dare enter the tent.

As she approached, the flap lifted and her chief minister emerged. Tura cracked a wide, blackened smile. "He still hasn't come?"

Cotota shook her head. "No. And if we don't see his caravan on the horizon in the morning, he won't be here tomorrow either." She tugged her robes tighter to shield against the wind, as she cast one last anxious gaze at the horizon. The moment Dogar appeared, her time as regent would be over. Geser and Dogar would go to war over the right to be the next *khan*, and any good that Cotota had forged in the four years she had been regent would be as forgotten as the day's sun.

"Then there's still more time."

Cotota let her serene face slip, just slightly. Just enough to show Tura the worry in her eyes. "At least two more days."

"We must hurry with the weaving then."

"Have the women gathered?"

Tura nodded and held up the tent flap. Cotota ducked her head as she entered the tent and observed the women gathered. Four dozen of the empire's strongest, most cunning women stood before her. Armor gleamed in the candlelight. Weapons were honed to sharp points. Stacks of arrows and medical supplies lined walls, and in the very back, she heard the sharp pounding of metal against metal as further weapons were forged.

"We have at least two days before my son arrives," Cotota announced. "We must be ready, for we will slay them. Gesar. Dogar. Anyone who challenges my right to the khanate. We will be a kingdom of women, and we will be the ones to forge the peace our men have ignored. We are the punishment that the gods has sent to purge the great sins of man. We will finish the work that the Great Khan, Genghis, began on Earth."

As the world of men waited outside for their next khan, every woman in the tent clasped her hands together and bowed to their true leader.

MIKE SCHULTZ · 2016 IN HOMAGE TO RENÉ BULL AND NICHOLAS ROERICH

73

NATE BEAR

AILA
...

VALORA
...

BAYUMI
...

I
WASN'T
READY.

KADEN,
ALWAYS REMEMBER
....

WE DON'T FIGHT.

WE DEFEND *LIFE*.

NO!!

AAAHHHH!

CHOMP!

ELEANOR AND JUNE
BY MERIDEL NEWTON

t's time to let go," she said softly, placing a hand on the back of the prone girl in front of her. "He's not coming back."

The girl looked up, and the unashamed tears streaking her face made her friend feel, somehow, blasphemous. "But he has to. He promised he'd never leave me."

The taller girl made a scornful sound and switched her grip to her friend's shoulder, tugging lightly upwards. "It was a fool's errand, Princess. A lost cause. We all knew he wouldn't make it."

"But he was supposed to!" The princess threw herself into her friend's arms. "He was my hero, the one suitor I fell in love with! The bold man and true! He was supposed to come back. June, what am I going to do now?"

June frowned. "You really loved him? When you knew him for less than a day?"

The princess paused to think about that. "Well, he was very handsome."

"Yes," June agreed, "he was that."

"And he was a seventh son of a seventh son." The princess made this declaration like it was irrefutable evidence of... something. "So it had to be him."

June considered this. "Well," she said slowly, "I'm the seventh daughter of a seventh daughter. But you don't love me just because of that, do you?"

"Oh no, of course not!" The princess exclaimed, raising her head from where she'd buried it in her friend's bosom. "I love you for so very many reasons! Because we have known each other for years and years and years, and never had a fight!"

"Well, you are a very virtuous princess," said June modestly. "It would be difficult to fight with you."

"And," the princess continued passionately, "you have looked after me for ever so long. You are wise and brave and fierce, and you beat the men in the yard at sword practice every time! Why June, if you were only a boy, I'd marry you!"

"Don't be silly, Nora. You couldn't marry me. I wouldn't be a knight or a prince, even if I were a boy." The girl smiled at her princess, wistful.

"Details," said the princess dismissively.

"Details?" June asked, an eyebrow cocked and the kernel of an idea beginning to take shape.

"Details," said the princess firmly, and she was no longer even sniffling. "You can become a prince with a wish."

"A wish. If that's all," June said, "is it really such a problem that I am not a boy?" She stood, a thoughtful gleam in her eyes.

"Oh June, you mustn't," exclaimed the princess. "The challenge is very dangerous. Thirty-two princes have died already!"

"Then," said June, "Perhaps it is a good thing that I am not a prince."

"But I might lose you! June, I couldn't stand that!"

June smiled gently down at her friend. "I swear to you, my lady, you will never lose me. I will find that wish, and I will meet the challenge."

Slow light dawned in Nora's eyes. "Then we could be married," she whispered. "And we'd never be apart!"

June smiled at her friend. "Indeed."

The challenge set for the princess's suitors had been very carefully chosen by her father. King Harold was reluctant to let his daughter go, and so had chosen something that he thought would be impossible for all but the bravest and most valiant man alive. And that, he knew, he was unlikely to get from the current crop of eligible princes. If things went as he expected them to, he'd have his daughter by his side well into his old age and retirement.

The kingdom of Minniver consisted in large part of sandy shoreline, and as such was a thriving maritime society. It had not only a capital city, but three other sizable ports as well. The kingdom was long and narrow, backed tightly against a range of mountains that ran along the coast of the continent. The northernmost city traded with the kingdom to the north for furs, soft woods, and delicate crafts while the southernmost city traded with the southern neighbor for fruits, nuts, and fine light fabrics. The central city traded with the other two cities and sent the best and most expensive of the goods up the river to the capitol, set on a high plateau before the mountains.

All of which would have worked perfectly and made for a thriving, secure country but for two small issues. Minniver was at war, and had been for most of her long existence. The eastern mountains hosted a colony of dragons who felt the crawling creatures on the flanks of their home were little more than a parasitic threat to be wiped out, and thus had spent hundreds of years killing every human to venture very far into the range. For this reason, no pass had ever been found through the mountains, though the king longed to expand his trade routes into the kingdom to the east.

In addition, the merpeople of the ocean hated and resented the humans for their encroachment onto what they considered their domain. The large wooden ships the people of Minniver built were awkward and clumsy upon the waves, and more often than not destroyed precious coral reefs instead of navigating around them. The sailors were arrogant and uncaring, dumping their waste into the water as though no one lived there. Worst of all, the fishermen's nets caught unwary merchildren, who were then never seen again. This state of affairs had continued until the merking had banned humans from entering his waters altogether. Now if a ship ventured too far from the coast, the merpeople attacked and destroyed it, dooming her sailors to a watery grave.

The king of Minniver was beyond frustrated with these limitations on his kingdom. He wanted to explore and expand. He wanted trade with the rich countries of the east, and he wanted his brave sailors discovering new lands and treasures to the west. But all attempts to defeat the dragons and the merfolk had failed. He had lost platoons of good soldiers to them both, and it didn't seem to matter how well he armed the knights he sent out, because none of them ever came back.

The old king loved his daughter very much, but he was also a crafty man. He figured that if he had to lose her eventually, he may as well gain something he had always longed for in exchange. And so the impossible task he set for his daughter's suitors was obvious– they simply had to remove one of the obstacles to his kingdom's growth. The favored prince who could neutralize the threat of either the dragons or the merfolk would be allowed to marry his beautiful, sweet daughter.

The challenge had been in place for two years, ever since the princess had turned sixteen. Word of her beauty and goodness had spread throughout the surrounding countries, and princes came from far and wide to see her for themselves. Inevitably they fell in love with her and vowed to take up the challenge, but the princess (whose full name was Eleanor), only gave permission to those she felt to truly have a chance of success. She knew all too well the impossibility of the task her father had set, and her kind heart could not stand to let such brave and gallant men go to their inevitably messy deaths.

This was why she could not allow her dear friend June to follow the thirty-two dead men. "But you mustn't take the challenge," she declared, "I couldn't bear to lose you."

June smiled a small, secret smile. "Don't worry about me, Your Highness. I'll be fine." And she turned and retreated to her palace rooms, leaving June to fret over her surely dire fate.

The next day, a new suitor presented himself to the Princess Eleanor and the court. Clad from head to foot in shining golden armor, he cut a striking figure, standing tall and proud before the gathered nobility. His sword was short but finely made, and his shield bore the device of a lioness rampant.

"Oooh," breathed the ladies, "isn't he fine? Look how slim he his! And his legs are just lovely."

"Hmph," sniffed the men, "He looks a bit short to me. And he can't be very strong with such thin shoulders."

"Your Highness," called the knight, in a fine, clear voice. "I beg your leave to take up your father's challenge and win your hand in marriage."

"Oh," the princess sighed. "I'm sure you do, sir, but I have decided not to grant anyone my permission anymore. No one ever seems to come back alive, and the really determined ones don't seek my permission anyway."

There was a smothered gasp from the court, but the knight rallied beautifully. "Nevertheless, my lady. I would have your blessing in my undertaking."

The princess sniffed. "What good would it do you, sir? I won't put a blessing on your death."

The golden knight swept the princess a deep bow. "Nora," he said, his voice so low the courtiers leaned forward to hear it, "I swear I will return to you."

The princess gasped, bringing one small, dark hand to her shapely lips. "Oh," she said softly, for there was only one person who called her that, "that's different then."

"My lady?" The armored figure remained bowed.

"Very well, sir knight," she called. "You may go take up this challenge. But I will hold you to your oath."

The knight smiled behind the helmet. "I shall not break my word, my lady." And he turned and strode from the court, leaving a whirl of rumor behind him.

 he golden knight (who was, of course, June) left the court quickly, wishing to avoid any questions. She thought she might journey first to the mountains to seek the dragons—if she were to be killed on this quest, the dragons were more likely to make a it a quick death. And she'd rather be immolated than drowned any day—it was warmer.

hmm'd quietly to herself. "I've been thinking. Even if you do this, June, you're still not a prince. Not even a knight."

June shook her head. "Your father has plenty of land. He could give me a small kingdom to call my own before the wedding. Isn't that what he planned to do for the tailor?"

"Such a strong tailor. Seven in one blow! What do you think happened to him?"

June shrugged as she strapped on the last of her armor. "Same as happened to the other thirty-one suitors, I expect."

"Oh, June," Eleanor sighed, her eyes looking distant and thoughtful.

"I'll be fine, Nora. Don't worry so much." June shook her head, her golden hair whipping about. "Could you pin all this up for me? I can't really raise my arms."

Eleanor smiled. "Of course."

They set out at last, June in full armor and Eleanor in a pair of dun trousers that would have been quite scandalous back at court. When she saw June pick up her shield, Eleanor insisted on carrying the suitcase. June couldn't quite bring herself to refuse even though proper knightly etiquette would have required it.

"Why don't you wear your boots?" Eleanor asked.

"They were too hot, and stones kept getting stuck in them," June answered.

"So you took them off? Very wise."

June nodded and said nothing.

A few minutes later, Eleanor asked, "You really can't raise your arms above your head?"

June raised an arm to demonstrate, nearly impaling her neck with a spiked pauldron. "Armor wasn't designed for mobility."

"Hm. If you can do without the boots, why not the pauldrons? Or any of it? You'd be faster."

"I would, but…" June frowned. She needed the armor for protection, didn't she? She couldn't be the first suitor to fail because the dragon just bit her in two. "I need it all."

"But the helmet blocks your vision! You need to be able to see, don't you?"

"I can see fine, Nora."

"I'm just saying, the armor doesn't seem very practical in this case."

"Would you like to see the dragon claw me open?"

"Of course not! June..."

So caught up were they in the discussion that they nearly missed the cave. The path they followed led straight past its mouth, which appeared as a simple hole in the mountainside overhung with roots and grasses. The gaping darkness invited neither visitors nor curiosity, and a faint smell of brimstone leaked from the chasm, causing Nora to wrinkle her nose in disgust.

Well. There was a correct way to proceed, and June was determined to do these things properly. She buckled her shield, drew her sword, and turned to Eleanor.

"Get back," she said. "Behind those rocks. Stay hidden!"

Eleanor nodded silently and did just that, ducking behind an outcropping of dark granite.

Only when she was satisfied the princess was safely out of the way did June turn and march to the cave mouth. Was there a standard thing to say in this situation? If she'd been a real knight, she'd have known.

That couldn't be helped now. She redoubled her grip on the sword hilt and called, "Dragon! Come out and answer for your wrongs!"

It had sounded impressive in her head, but the silence which greeted her pronouncement made her feel foolish. Perhaps this was not a dragon's cave. Perhaps it had been empty for years. The tales of knights with noble deeds never included just how they'd found those noble deeds.

Long moments passed. Just as she was about to give up and go find another cave to shout at, a great racket arose from the dark.

June froze in her stance of challenge. It would not do, now, to be caught with second thoughts. She set her jaw and waited for the beast to appear.

There was a scraping sound, dry and whispery and full of sharp edges. She could almost see the scales being dragged across stone. Then came a long, moaning bellow, as the smell grew stronger and a sudden haze thickened in the air.

"What are these wrongs of which you speak, knight?" came a deep, booming voice.

June leaned into her sword to hide her trembling. "The deaths of many a brave prince and innocent tradesman, and the menace your kind present to the kingdom."

"No man I killed was innocent, and they certainly weren't brave by the end," the dragon responded. And though June drew breath to answer, it caught in her throat as the creature came into view at last.

The dragon was, to be honest, smaller than she might have thought. And maybe a bit run-down, in a strange way. The scales along spine and neck were disheveled and uneven, hanging out at all angles and definitely not lying flush to the body as she had imagined they would. The beast might once have been a brilliant red, but an impressive collection of scratches and encrusted dirt dulled the color to a muddy carmine. A film covered one eye, giving the creature a strange, milky gaze. Nonetheless that good eye turned to June, and she felt herself caught in a piercing stare.

"I see you have no intention of breaking that trend," the creature remarked with dry wit.

The cut recalled June to herself. She had come here with a purpose, and she intended to fulfill it. She straightened up and held the sword before her. "You will find appearances deceiving in my case, dragon," she proclaimed, and she started toward the creature.

The dragon flicked its tail negligently and spread ragged wings. "If you are claiming to be more than you seem, knight, I have heard that one before. You all taste the same to me."

June lunged forward, the sword aimed directly at the monster's heart. The dragon dodged aside easily, moving far faster than she would have thought possible. She paused to reassess her attack as the dragon chuckled.

"All you soft-skins so slow and clumsy. You never seem to learn from all your losses." So saying, the dragon swept a long tail over wings and shoulders and stabbed downward.

In that moment, June reassessed her plan of attack. She dropped her shield and dodged the tail nimbly, suddenly grateful she had neglected to replace the heavy golden boots. Then, in the same movement, she ducked behind the spread wings, hearing the brush of the vanes against her helmet. Flush with her triumph, she turned and rested the point of her sword in the soft, disordered scales between the creature's wing joints.

The dragon froze. "This is different. And hardly chivalrous, to attack from behind."

"You'll find my grasp on chivalry to be lacking," she replied, leaning harder on the sword.

"Along with your grasp on proper footwear." The dragon turned, scales rattling against the blade, and executed some sort of combination wingstroke and flip maneuver that launched it into the air to land ahead of her on the path. The two opponents faced each other once again.

"I've found it more practical," June replied, somehow feeling the need to defend her choices to the dragon.

"So very practical," the dragon said, clearly mocking her. "You are the soul of realism, I expect."

"If I were a realist, I wouldn't be here."

The dragon smiled as though this were the correct response. Then, with a great sweep of ragged wings, it rose into the air and inhaled. The next second, a great gout of flame poured from its mouth, streaming down toward the small golden knight.

June had no shield, but she did have good boots. She turned and ran, throwing herself off the path just at the edge of the flame. Her sword went flying into the brush and she landed hard on one shoulder. When her own downhill momentum flipped her onto her back, the air rushed from her lungs.

For a brief moment, a surreal expanse of cloudless sky was all she could see. Then a huge, scaly head thrust into view and a weight fell across her chest and legs. Only her armor saved her ribs from cracking as the dragon leaned forward, foul breath filtering through the helmet's visor.

"Thirty-three," the beast said, and opened a great toothy maw.

"No!" The shriek startled them both, and the dragon actually looked away to identify the source.

For a moment nothing changed. Then Princess Eleanor stepped out from behind her rocky shelter, looking small and scared and fiercely determined.

"Nora, no," June managed.

"Please," Eleanor said. Her voice trembled. "Please, don't hurt her."

"Her?" the dragon's voice managed to make a sibilant hiss of a word with no 's'.

"Yes, her. Please, dragon. She's my best friend. My only friend, and the one I intend to marry. Just… please."

She was crying now. June struggled against the great taloned foot holding her down, and was somewhat surprised to feel it lift, just a bit.

"Nora, get out of here. Run!" she called.

Eleanor didn't listen. Instead, she approached the dragon with tiny, hesitating steps. The dragon leaned back as she came, a strange look on the great lizardy face, and lifted the foot restraining June until she could almost wriggle free.

Eleanor reached June and knelt down, her fingers scrabbling at the base of the helmet.

"What are you doing? You have to go!" June protested.

"Shhh," Eleanor replied. "I think I'm saving your life."

She worked the helmet free, and June lifted her head as it came off. Her hair had come loose in the fight, and it fell from the helmet in a golden cascade.

"See?" Eleanor said. "She's a woman. Not a knight. And we've learned our lesson. Please, dragon, if you let us go, I… I can promise you no more princes or knights will ever come up here to kill you."

The dragon squinted at her uncertainly. "I don't see what the gender of the soft-skin trying to kill me has to do with anything. If there's armor and a sword, it's a knight."

"Oh, no," Eleanor said, her eyes widening. "That's not at all what makes a knight. Knights are specially chosen, and they train for years, and they have to be knighted."

"Knighted." If a dragon's tone could possibly be flat, this one achieved it.

"Right." Eleanor wrapped an arm around June's shoulders. "That's when a member of the royal family makes you officially a knight."

"Hmmm…" The dragon lowered its head to look at the two of them on their level. It was, if anything, even more fearsome up close. "You are saying this… woman acted on no authority, then?"

"Ah…" Eleanor hesitated. "No. She acted on my authority."

A great blast of hot air swept over them. The dragon had snorted. "And what authority do you have, little soft-skin? Why should I believe you have the power to promise anything at all?"

Eleanor stood and drew herself up to her full, unimposing height. She lifted her chin and her voice, and even in ugly trous she still somehow managed to look regal.

"I am Princess Eleanor of Minniver. On my honor, dragon, if you let my friend live, I will put an end to the bounty on your life."

"A princess!" At this, the dragon at last released June entirely. It somehow sounded pleased. With supernatural speed, it circled quickly around Eleanor, examining her from every angle.

"Hrm." The dragon was peering at her doubtfully. "I've never seen a princess in pants before."

"It's a disguise," Eleanor replied, sounding defensive.

"It works."

She tried to ignore the implication. "Do we have a deal then, dragon?"

The dragon stepped away, and the ridges of its face moved to suggest a frown. "No."

"No?"

"No." A claw slammed down on June's loose helmet, punching through the metal as though it were paper. "You have promised not to send any further soft-skins after me. This is all very well, but it does nothing to safeguard my friends and family. Furthermore, I have no reason to expect you will keep your word once you have returned to your cave."

"My word is unimpeachable!" cried Eleanor, and at the same time June managed, "There are more of you?"

"Your word has sanctioned thirty-three attempts to kill me," the dragon said. "And of course there are more dragons. Most of us live much deeper in the mountains, of course, but I always have preferred the excitement of the uncivilized frontier."

"More dragons..." June muttered, staring at the remains of her beautiful golden helmet.

"And if a knight needs royal authority to be a knight, and you are royal and gave this woman authority, then she is a knight," the dragon continued. "Or do you not have that... authority?"

Eleanor frowned. "What would it take to convince you that my word is good?"

"A treaty," the dragon answered.

"A treaty?" Eleanor repeated.

"Between you and the Dragon Council."

"There's a council?" June said. "Oh, hooray."

 he Council met, as would be expected, in a cavern deep in the mountains. Eleanor and June arrived sore and angry, covered in scrapes and bruises acquired while sliding down steep slopes and hacking through brambles. Their dragon had led them there, but they had followed on the ground while it flew above and made snarky remarks about their speed. June had lost her pauldrons, greaves, and vambraces during the trek, opting for mobility over impenetrability. She had rather lost confidence in her armor's ability to protect her after the destruction of her helmet, anyhow.

Nonetheless, they arrived in most of one piece each, and the dragon made a slow and considerate landing before the cavern entrance.

"Wait here," their guide said. "I will call the council." Head, wings, and tail disappeared into the mountain with a deadly grace.

June fixed Eleanor with a considering look. "We could probably escape now," she said, her tone casual.

"Probably," Eleanor agreed.

June waited, but Eleanor didn't seem to have anything else to say, so she elected not to push the issue.

Too soon the dragon reemerged, fixing them with the one good eye. "They are ready for you," came the announcement

Eleanor led the way, her chin raised in her most haughty, princessly demeanor. June followed at her shoulder, though she little knew what good she could do.

Inside, the cavern was enormous. A great vaulted space met their surprised gazes, lit by gentle phosphorescence which seemed to emerge from the rock walls themselves. Massive columns reached from floor to ceiling, and the walls...

The walls were lined with dragons. Dragons great and small and of all colors of the rainbow, they rustled their wings and tapped their talons and switched their tails as Eleanor and June walked past. Their eyes caught the light, reflecting it back in greens and reds and yellows far brighter than seemed possible.

Eleanor marched straight ahead, unhesitating, and June could only follow her lead. Soon they came to the back of the cavern, where the three largest dragons awaited them on a raised platform in the stone. Red, green, and blue, they each wore a simple golden circlet around their necks.

The red one spoke first. "This is the princess?"

"Which one?" asked the blue.

"Neither one looks like a princess," added the green one.

Eleanor cleared her throat. "I am Princess Eleanor of Minniver."

"Minniver?" asked the red, though all three of them looked baffled. "What's that?"

"It's my kingdom."

"Kingdom?" the green one said. "And where exactly is this kingdom of Minniver?"

"It's here," Eleanor said, and June could tell she'd been thrown off her stride. "Here, and the lands west of here to the sea."

"Oh, we're in a kingdom?" the blue one said. "So good of them to tell us."

"Did you hear that?" the red one asked, directing the question to the gathered crowd. "We're part of a kingdom."

A sibilant hissing filled the cave, which June took to be the sound of nearly a hundred dragons laughing.

The green one raised fixed Eleanor with a pointed gaze, and June was reminded of a particularly steely governess for her youth. She wondered if this dragon was female. "And why have you come, little soft-skin princess?" the dragon asked.

Eleanor raised her chin, attempting to meet each of the six eyes of the Council in succession. "I want to offer a treaty."

"A treaty!" the red one said. "What sort of treaty could we possibly want with this so-called kingdom?"

"I think we should hear her out," the green one said, and the blue one nodded in agreement.

Eleanor swallowed, gathering her courage, and launched into her argument.

June stood a few feet back from her friend, watching in admiration. The Council seemed willing enough to make the treaty, and though they frequently displayed their many teeth and flexed their many claws, Eleanor did not seem shaken by the intimidation tactics. She forged ahead, laying out the advantage both dragons and humans stood to gain with open travel routes and communication between them. She solemnly swore that she would honor the terms of the contract, and that she spoke for her father, the king, as well. And though the Council seemed to find the very idea of hereditary monarchy amusing, they accepted her claims.

"So," said the green one at last. "The terms stand at this: humans may pass freely through our lands so long as they stay on the designated route. Any human found off these routes is fair game for sport and food, as is any fool who thinks to kill himself a dragon. We shall establish official communications between the Council and the king, and treat as neighboring countries."

"Agreed," said the blue dragon.

"I still think we should just continue as we were," the red one said. "Some of these soft-skins can be delicious."

"But this agreement will benefit us all," said the green dragon. "Let's put it to a vote."

Dragons, apparently, voted with their fiery breath. When Eleanor and June reemerged from the column they had sheltered behind, the green dragon beamed at them.

"Well, my dear, it appears you have your treaty."

"Good," said Eleanor. "And I have one more small request..."

nce they were well clear of the cavern, Eleanor turned to June and wrapped her arms around her. The princess's head lowered to rest on June's shoulder, but then she stepped back with a frustrated sound.

"Nora? What is it?"

"Your armor," Eleanor replied, wrinkling her nose. "It... doesn't make this easy."

June looked down at herself. Over the course of the journey, she'd shed so much of her armor she had only her breastplate left. It had once shone, but now it looked dusty and battered. The low sun picked out faint hints of gold beneath the grime.

With a rueful sigh, she fumbled at the buckles on one side.

"Here, let me help," Eleanor said eagerly. Her nimble fingers made short work of the buckle, and the armor fell away, revealing the soft shirt she wore underneath. June shivered, feeling strangely exposed.

"Better," Eleanor said, grinning. She gave her friend an appraising look, and her smile turned sly.

"What is it?" June asked.

Eleanor shook her head. "Just... happy to see you."

This time when they hugged, there was nothing but warmth and love between them. It was a long time before they each let the other go, but at last they did. They smiled softly at each other and turned, hands still clasped tightly, to make their way down the trail.

"What is it that you asked for, there at the end?" June asked.

Eleanor grinned, reached into a pocket, and pulled out the trinket. A polished silver coin hung from a chain, and in the late evening light it shimmered and glittered so brightly it was hard to look at.

"And what is it?" June asked again.

"Our wish," Eleanor replied.

"Our..." June caught her breath.

"Here," Eleanor said, handing it to her. "Blow on it."

June frowned, but she trusted her princess. Her friend. Her love. She raised the coin to her lips and blew.

A flash of light blinded the two girls, and Eleanor threw her hands up with a cry to shield her face. June just managed to remember to hold on to the necklace as she did the same. When the light faded and they dared to lower their hands, they gaped in astonishment: glimmering at the end of the chain, the coin had become a small, bright fairy, fluttering in midair.

"A fairy!" June cried.

"We have dragons and mermaids, so why not?" Eleanor said brightly.

"So, does this mean the fairy grants the wish?"

The tiny creature coughed delicately, and they leaned in to hear her as she spoke.

"You..." said the fairy, "you have half a wish."

"Half a wish!" cried June. "What is that?"

"Budget cuts," replied the fairy.

"No, it's all right," Eleanor said, "I read a book like this."

"Like this?" June asked.

"It's this book where... never mind." Eleanor turned to the fairy. "Any limits?"

"Fairy magic has no limits," came the sniffy reply.

"All right," Eleanor said, "I wish for two more wishes."

"Done," the fairy replied instantly. "You have one wish."

Eleanor smiled in triumph at June. "See? I know this."

"Magic wishes always go wrong," June muttered.

"It shouldn't be that hard," Eleanor said, "Just don't start any sentence with 'I wish' until we have the right wording."

"I wish it were that simple," June said, rolling her eyes.

"Done," said the fairy, sounding smug.

Eleanor stared at her, aghast. June clapped her hands to her mouth. "Oh, Nora," she whispered. Then she rallied and cried, "That isn't fair! It wasn't my wish!"

"...what?" asked the fairy.

"It wasn't my wish. You said Eleanor had one wish, not me."

The fairy's eyes widened. "But... okay, then you still have one wish."

"No," June said, "My wish came true, right? Because it really is as simple as not saying 'I wish'?"

"Yes..." said the fairy. She frowned. "I'm going to get in trouble for this, aren't I?"

"It's okay," Eleanor said, wrapping an arm around June's waist, "I can fix this. Look," she picked up a nearby stick and, bending to write in the dirt, wrote an X. "Here," she said. "This is June, because she has no wishes."

"Hey!" June protested.

Eleanor ignored her and wrote X+1. "This is me," she said. "Because I'm supposed to have one wish, right?"

"Right..." said the fairy suspiciously.

"Right," June confirmed.

Eleanor wrote X+1=1. "So, look, I'm supposed to have one wish, right?"

The fairy nodded.

"But June had one wish, right?"

$X=1$

She nodded again.

"So, look," Eleanor said. "If X is one, then X plus one has to be..."

"Two!" the fairy cried.

"Right," Eleanor said. "Give me two wishes and you'll be fine."

"Well..." The fairy frowned, her forehead deeply furrowed as she thought. "All right..."

"Right," Eleanor smiled in triumph. "My first wish is that you don't see the flaw in that logic until it's too late. And my second wish is for June and I to be at our wedding. Right now."

And so they were.

TARA HELFER

ROSE BOYLE

Be the Knight You Want to Be!

Instructions: Cut pieces along dotted line and dress your knight however you want to reflect your inner badass self!

ALMOND?

IT'S TRUE THAT WE HAVE SEEN MANY KNIGHTS, THOUGH NONE SO SMALL AS YOU.

BUT THOUGH YOU MAY BE THE FIRST OF YOUR KIND...

5.4.2450

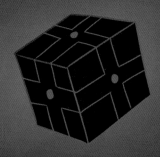

ART AND STORY BY NIKA

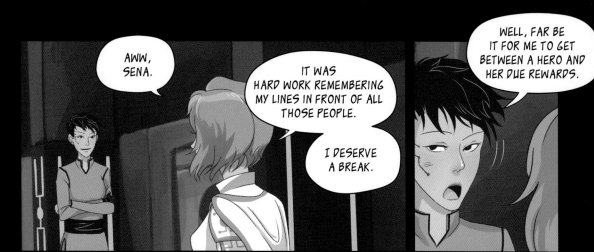

155

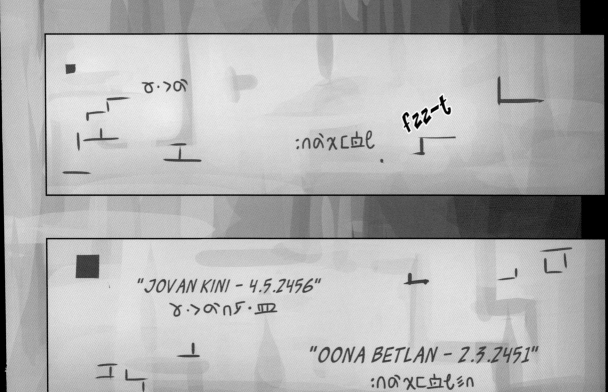

"JOVAN KINI – 4.5.2456"

"OONA BETLAN – 2.3.2451"

MOST PEOPLE, WHEN THEY SEE "DO NOT ENTER", DO NOT ENTER.

ACK!

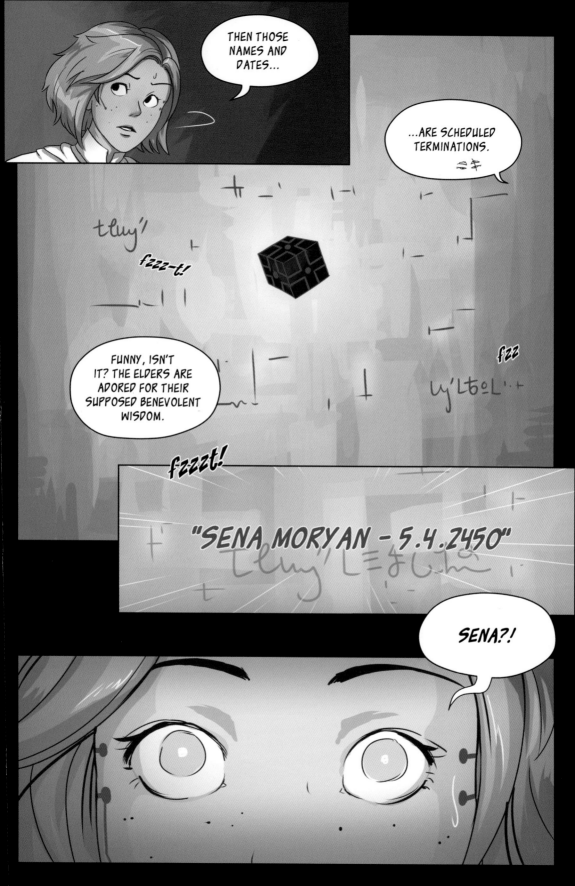

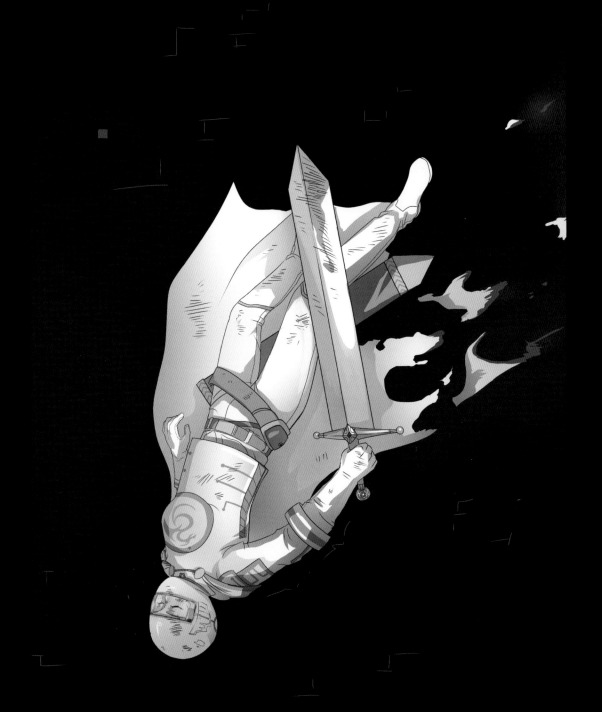

Super Love People

by Kevin Mutch

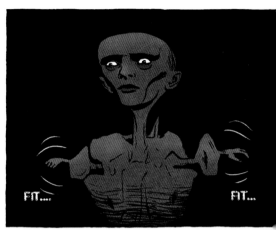

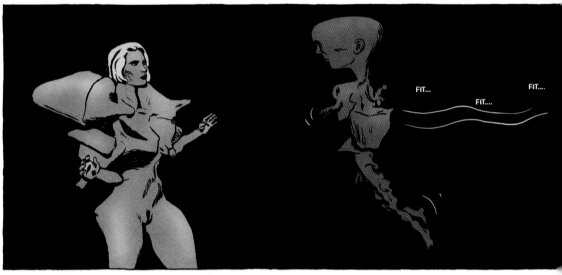

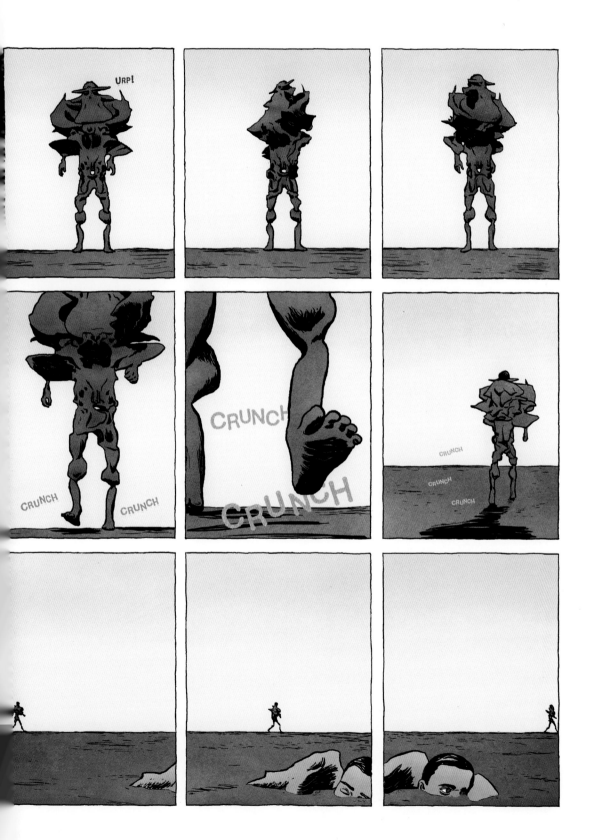

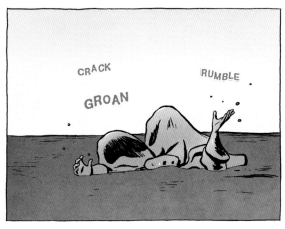

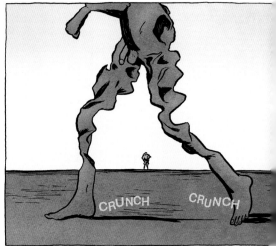

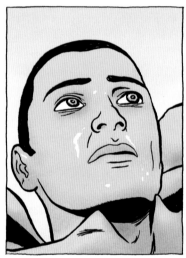

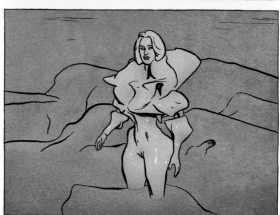

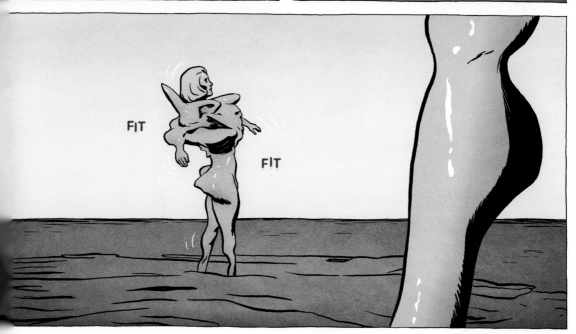

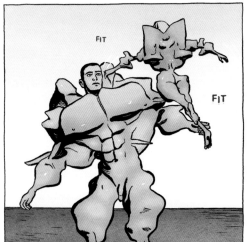

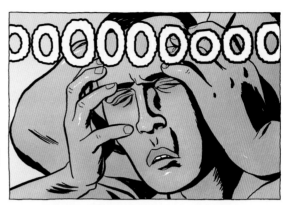

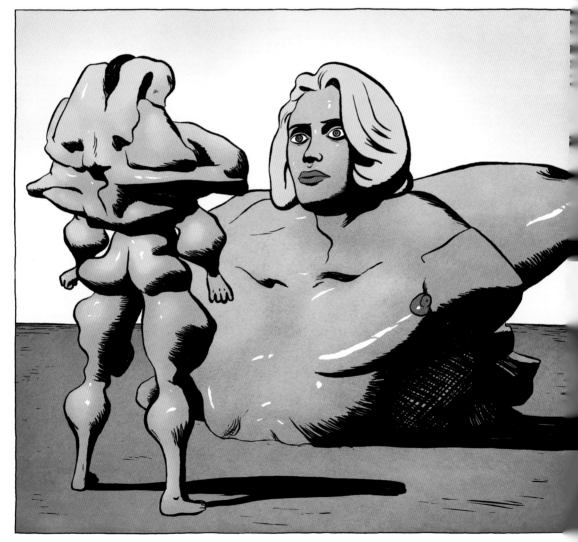

CRUNCH   CRUNCH

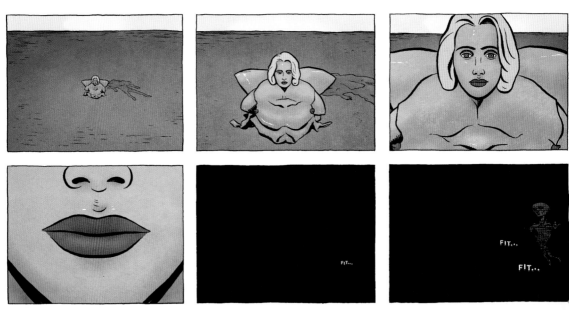

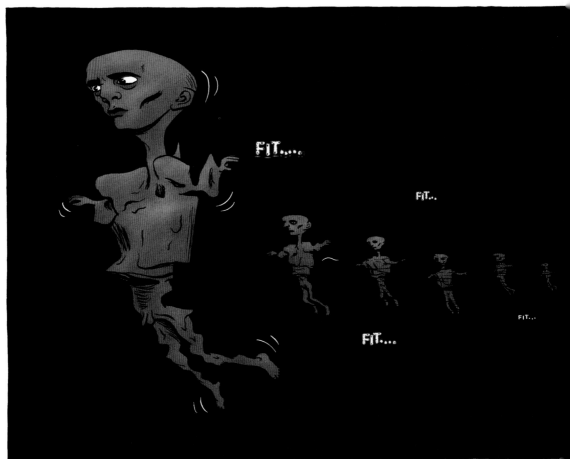

185

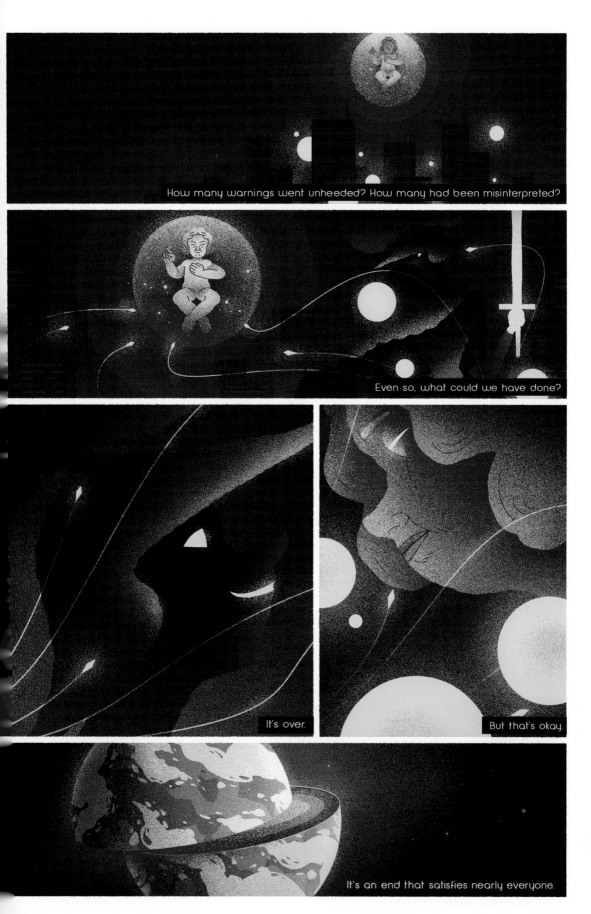

LADY ROBERTA

COASTAL KNIGHT & GUARD OF THE SHORE

LIKE ALL CAPE WITCHES, LADY ROBERTA LIVES IN A LIGHTHOUSE AND SPEAKS TO THE SEA. SHE SET UP SHOP ON THE TIDAL ISLAND OF FOX POINT, AND WITH A KING'S BLESSING SHE WATCHES OVER THE SHORE. THE PEOPLE OF CAPE WILLOW SAY THE WILL OF THE OCEAN IS THE WHIM OF LADY ROBERTA, THAT SHE CALMS THE WAVES FOR WORTHY SAILORS AND CALMS THE LOST SOULS STRANDED AT SEA. THEY ALSO SAY SHE'S A SEA MONSTER IN HUMAN FORM, AND THAT SHE DROWNS A SHIP HERE AND THERE TO FEED HER FISH KIN.

IN HER DAY TO DAY DUTIES AS A COASTAL KNIGHT, SHE CARRIES THESE —

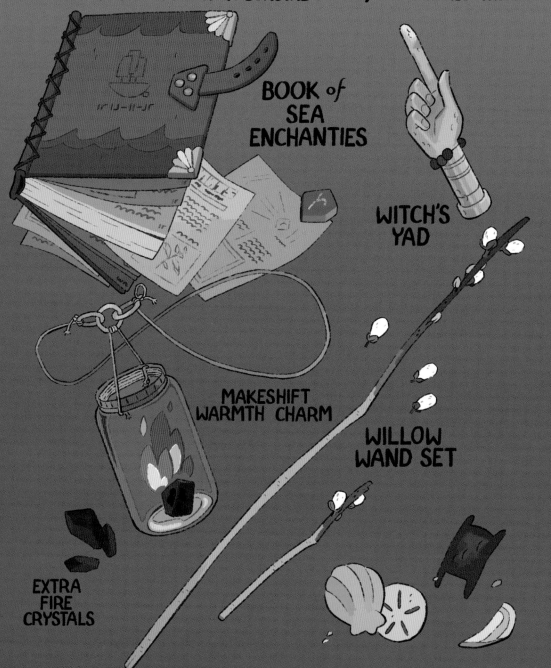

THE MYTH OF MEDUSA

BY RYAN NORTH W/ART BY KEVIN JAY STANTON

ONCE UPON A TIME THERE WAS A LADY NAMED MEDUSA, WHO A LOT OF PEOPLE FOUND CONVENTIONALLY ATTRACTIVE!

ANYWAY, ONE TIME SHE HAD SOME FUN SEX WITH A DUDE. NO BIG DEAL, RIGHT?

HEY BOYS! I'M THE KIND OF HOTNESS SOCIETY TELLS YOU TO LIKE!

BUT IT TURNED OUT THAT ATHENA (A LITERAL GOD) DID ACTUALLY THINK IT WAS A BIG DEAL, BECAUSE ALL THAT FUN SEX HAPPENED INSIDE HER TEMPLE.

NO HAVING SEX IN HERE

WHAT IS WRONG WITH YOU?? THIS IS BASICALLY A CHURCH, HELLO

STOP IMAGINING NAKED PEOPLE AND COME HERE TO THINK ABOUT RELIGION AND STUFF FOR ONCE IN YOUR LIVES

MEDUSA! FROM NOW ON YOUR FACE WILL TURN ANY LIVING THING INTO STONE!

THIS PUNISHMENT SEEMS...ENTIRELY UNRELATED TO MY ALLEGED "CRIME"?

COMPLAIN AGAIN AND I'LL TURN YOUR HAIR INTO SNAKES!

I—

TOO LATE, ENJOY HAVING TO FEED YOUR HAIR MICE FOREVER NOW

MEDUSA WAS NOW THE SINGLE GREATEST BIOLOGICAL WEAPON ON THE PLANET.

THIS IS...

...UH, ACTUALLY KIND OF AWESOME??

SINCE MEDUSA WAS A SMART COOKIE, SHE QUICKLY WORKED TO GAIN CONTROL OF HER POWER.

AND ONCE SHE'D DONE THAT, SHE WENT INTO BUSINESS.

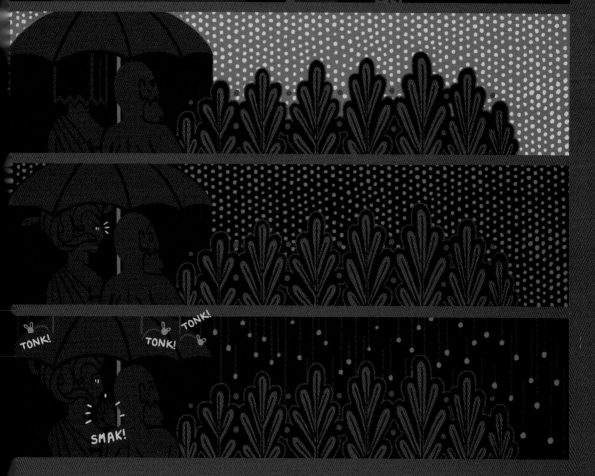

YARR, MY BOAT'S GOT RATS IN HER HOLD!

I'VE GOT LICE IN MY HAIR!

LET ME SEE.

MY DRINKING WATER HAS BACTERIA IN IT!

THERE! NOW THERE'S JUST EXTREMELY TINY BACTERIA-SHAPED ROCKS AT THE BOTTOM OF YOUR GLASS INSTEAD.

NOW THAT'S AN OBJECTIVE IMPROVEMENT!!

EVENTUALLY MEDUSA MARRIED A MAN WHO DIDN'T CARE IF HE COULD NEVER SEE HER FACE (MAINLY BECAUSE HE COULD STILL SMOOCH IT AS LONG AS HE KEPT HIS EYES CLOSED)

(AND BESIDES, HER SNAKE HAIR GAVE THINGS AN ELEMENT OF DANGER WHICH HE FOUND VERY ATTRACTIVE)

AND SHE LIVED HAPPILY EVER AFTER, AND WAS ALSO VERY RICH AND POPULAR.

OH, AND ONE TIME THIS JERK PERSEUS TRIED TO KILL HER. HE THOUGHT HIS MIRRORED SHIELD WOULD LET HIM LOOK AT MEDUSA'S FACE, BUT INDIRECTLY, SO THAT WAY HE WOULDN'T TURN TO STONE!

BUT MEDUSA'S POWER OBVIOUSLY WASN'T NULLIFIED BY MIRRORS BECAUSE THAT'S SILLY, AND SO HE DIED.

HER ENEMIES TRIED TO SPREAD MALICIOUS RUMOURS ABOUT HER, BUT THEY FAILED, AND SO HISTORY ALWAYS REMEMBERED MEDUSA AS THIS REALLY AWESOME LADY WITH A PARTICULARLY SWEET SUPERPOWER.

THE END

247

To the courageous & fantastic Kickstarter backers whose
generosity and support have made this book a reality,

THANK
YOU

All of your names will forever live in our hearts
and at onethousandandoneknights.com/thankyou

MEET THE KNIGHTS

The Knights of Wisdom were asked to define knighthood,
how they each gather strength and find sources of inspiration.

ACAMPORA, KRISTEN Pg. 222

To me, strength is the ability to persevere and keep your composure even under difficult circumstances.

www. kristenacampora.com   @kristenacampora   kristendraws.tumblr.com

ALMON, CLAIRE Pg. 11

When presented with the opportunity to share my ideas of strength and knighthood through the 1001 Knights project, I immediately looked to the examples in my own life for inspiration. One of the most inspiring pillars of strength in my life is my mother and the legacy of maternal strength in my family passed down through the generations. From an early age my mother has been the example of not only strength in the face of diversity (raising 5 children as a single mom) but also her resourcefulness, creativity and compassion, all of which she used to shield and protect her children in a harsh world. She sacrificed herself and her own needs many times in order to build us up into strong capable compassionate people. Putting our needs before her own was never a difficult decision for her even if it cost her blood, sweat and tears. Now as adults her children are armed with these values and strength with which they will shield and arm their own children or children in their lives. My mother still serves as an example of strength and selflessness as she continues to hold the family together but now I have the opportunity to witness the same beauty and strength manifest itself in the lives of my sisters and sister's-in-law as they continue to sacrifice and teach their own children. It makes me proud to be part of such a legacy of women. Women that survived the genocide in Armenia to plant their lives here in the United States with strength, grace, compassion, courage and love. In my illustration, my knight is an Armenian warrior woman based on the likeness of my own mother and maternal grandmother. She stands in the face of trial and difficulty guarding the future generations of women in my family. It is from her femininity that her strength and fierceness springs making her a force to be reckoned with. This is my way of paying homage to the knights in my life, the strong women who fight for and raise their families guarding and protecting them as any good knight would.

www.clairealmon.carbonmade.com   @clair3a   clairealmon.tumblr.com

ALDRIDGE, ETHAN Pg. 193

Strength, for me, is often a thing found in others. We find strength at the side of those we love, and it is no small courage to love in spite of fear.

www.ethanaldridge.weebly.com   @ethanmaldridge   estrangedstory.tumblr.com

ATOM, MAGNUS Pg. 85

"What has been will be again, what has been done will be done again; there is nothing new under the sun." Go to a library, visit a museum, take a walk in nature, travel, read a book. The world is full of inspirations you won't find behind a computer screen.

www.magnusatom.com   magnusatomart.tumblr.com

BAUMANN, BILLY Pg. 204

Strength is the power to overcome, to live, and to keep going. To say you want to do something and accomplishing it no matter the struggles you face. The ability to be yourself 100% and do what makes you happy uncaring of what people think of you. I think strength is a much more internal power and one that can affect and inspire so many people around you. Your life is your own and to have the power to live it the way you want to and make it through any hardships is true strength to me.

www.deliciousdesignleague.com/

BEAR, NATE Pg. 80-82

In my philosophy, strength is everything. Strength means achieving peace, by wearing thick armor to get you through the day. Armor so thick that it keeps out everything, all the criticism, all the anger, all of the sunshine and wind. Armor so thick that you can't move under its weight. You become impenetrable. Unseen. Shut off from the world. Become the armor. I am a mound of iron ore. There is no fleshy vulnerable core, only armor. You can't hurt me! I don't care what job Jacob has and he's only 24! I'm a hunk of solid bliss! Can Jacob do that, Huh!? Only once this state of tranquility is achieved, can one truly call oneself a knight.

www.natebearart.com   @natebear   natebear.tumblr.com

BLACK, HEIDI Pg. 28-35
As someone who has fairly severe depression, I know how much strength can be needed just to live. Some days it can be so hard not to just give up, but knowing how much that would hurt my family and friends gives me strength. I borrow their strength every day, and some day hope I can repay that with a strength of my own.

www.electricabyss.com   @electricabyss   heidiblack.tumblr.com

BOUCHER, AMANDA Pg. 37-40
I believe a character is strong when they understand themselves and always fight for what they want in life. A strong character will push forward and learn from mistakes along the way.

www.amanda-boucher.com   @MondarLynn

BOYLE, CAITLIN ROSE Pg. 135
Strength means taking care of your friends, never giving up, and always having time for snacks.

www.sadsadkiddie.com   @rattusRose   sadsadkiddie.tumblr.com

CANNIZZARO, LINDSAY Pg. 94-105
Strength is the ability to perservere, pushing through the hard times while holding on to the things that define us without succumbing to a place of darkness.

www.inkburststudios.deviantart.com   @licannizzaro

CHOO, F Pg. 84
Being strong is eating a raw egg every day

@chootalks   choodraws.tumblr.com

DABAIE, MARGUERITE Pg. 43
Strength can always be found in the stories of people, whether they lived thousands of years ago, or I just spoke with them last week. The strength I get from eating delicious food comes at a close second.

www.mdabaie.com   @mdabaie   panjikant.tumblr.com

DEZUTTI, CLARE Pg. 17
I think of a knight as a guardian. They act as a conduit for something or someone else. I think that's a special journey for a knight character- identifying who they are in relation to who they represent.

www.claredezutti.com   @claredez   claredezdraws.tumblr.com

DOUGHERTY, CAROLINE Pg. 44
To me, the strength of "knighthood" comes from human capacity for compassion and sacrifice—the ability and willingness to truly care for and protect someone who needs it.

www.thousandwrecks.com   cloven.tumblr.com

DRAGUNAS, JOE Pg. 72
I think Strength is fulfilling your desires, especially when it goes against the will of the world around which surrounds you. Not choosing to be different, but knowing you're different, and pursuing the goals that accompany your very soul.

jmdragunas.tumblr.com

DUVALL, SARA Pg. 42, 56-57, 83
I find strength in the princesses who choose to be their own knights in shining armor and slay a dragon.

saraduvall.tumblr.com

ECKMAN-LAWN, ALEX Pg. 52–55, 249

I think the toughest, strongest, most admirable thing anyone can do is to just be a good person no matter what. People who do what they know is right regardless of the circumstances, and support the people they believe in are so much more valuable to me than someone who can do a lot of pushups.

www.alexeckmanlawn.com @alexeckmanlawn dudenukem.tumblr.com

ECKWALL, JENSINE Pg. 74–75

Strength is knowing when to pick your battles. This sometimes means fighting at full force nonstop at whatever cost. More often than that it means knowing when to stop, whether for strategy's sake or because someone (oneself or another) is suffering because of that fighting.

www.jensineeckwall.com @whoisjensine jensineeckwall.tumblr.com

ELI, CARRIE Pg. 225

When I think about what strength means my mind automatically jumps to the beginning of a story, which is always my favorite part. You have these people, that for whatever reasons, decide to strike out on their own adventure. Starting a new journey is something new and unknown, you never know if you're going to succeed or fail. So for me, when I see or read about someone overcoming that fear and setting out to tackle whatever mission they've set before themselves I always feel like it shows an incredible amount of personal strength. Being able to step out of your comfort zone and try something new is strength to me.

www.carrieli.net

ELLIS, CANDACE Pg. 27

I'm not sure I have any right to say what is strong or not, but perhaps maybe motherhood is a form of strength. It must take great courage, even if one can't do very well, to be able to bring up a child in this world.

www.by-starlight.com @bybystarlight bybystarlight.tumblr.com

FERGUSON, LYNDA Pg. 58–61

A knight is any being that saves someone, though I feel that this archetype is always tragically flawed. The selfless ones never live long enough to save the world and the selfish ones are too self-involved to do the good they could. Yet I think both kinds can save someone even if in very different ways. Maybe they'll only save one person, be it themselves or another, but they'll have an impact on someone enough to change them forever.

@dacoffeeknight thatgirl120.tumblr.com

GARRISON, LANE Pg. 238–239

Strength for me has always been about having the courage to pursue your own path in spite of adversity.

@lanegarrisonart lane-garrison.tumblr.com

GRANT, MIKEY A. Pg. 62–69

To me a knight is someone with an unshakeable sense of self and duty. A knight poses a powerful desire to defend what they hold dear. Following a code crafted from their morals and views.

www.mgrantillustration.com @hungrypencils

GREEN, ALEXIS Pg. 132–133

A Knight is someone who has a great love in their heart. A Knight is willing to fight to protect that which brings light to their life. Being a Knight doesn't mean you are never beaten, but that you get back up more times than you are knocked down. You are a brave Knight; please be proud of yourself!

alioxinfri.tumblr.com @sprickles

GUSEV, VLAD Pg. 198–199

Strength is being confident in yourself and knowing that you can achieve absolutely anything.

www.vldgsv.com

HELFER, TARA Pg. 135

A strong character exercises agency, making decisions to control her own destiny, regardless of how short-sighted or small those decisions might be. It's also extremely cool if she can bench press a building, but that's totally not necessary!!

www.tarahelfer.com @thelfr tarahelfer.tumblr.com

HILLBURN, BECCA Pg. 87-90
To me, strength is the ability to push forward, even when the motivation is gone. The view never changes if you're always standing still.

www.beccahillburn.com @nattosoup nattosoup.tumblr.com

HKEZZA Pg. 206-207, 220-221
When I was a kid I've always admired where ordinary people transformed themselves to become a strong warrior. They freely give themselves to serve what's right and just, but they are hindered by what the world labels them. Being a fan of Joan of Arc, Brienne of Tarth (from Game of Thrones), I always admired that pinnacle moment they grasp a sword, or cut their hair, and redefine their identity. Once then, they find their real role, a defender, a warrior, a knight.

www.behance.net/kezzart @kezzart kezzart.tumblr.com

HOEWELER, MICHAEL Pg. 106
Strength is such a loaded word, and seems to be historically linked with possessing power. I strive to challenge that definition in myself and in my work and to interpret strength in a way that more closely resembles fortitude or resilience. This could manifest itself as facing hardship while acknowledging your fears and mustering as much courage as is possible. It could also be the ability to accept every facet of yourself, and to love yourself as a whole. For my character and myself, it means making the choice to care for and love others and yourself as fully and openly as possible, and to convey the beauty and strength found within vulnerability.

www.michaelhoeweler.com @michaelhoeweler michaelhoeweler.tumblr.com

HOWARD, SAGE Pg. 76-77
All the best heroes are hard workers.

www.sagehowardillustration.com @editedthought greylagoon.tumblr.com

HUMPHRIES, MAX Pg. 202-203
Strength to me comes through loyalty: Loyalty to your family and friends, loyalty to your ideals and loyalty to your craft.

www.maxhumphries.com @MaxHumphries instagram/MaxHumphriesPuppets

Photography by Jo Charlesworth

IGBOKWE, ODERA Pg. 107-111
read this in a Final Fantasy end game voice, or magical girl transformation sequence
I am a summoner of the memories spread across the aether. Conjurer of revolutions, movements, and resilience. My strength is the dance that unlocks the deities living inside of me. A dance that awakens realities that we must not forget.

www.odera.net @odyism odera.tumblr.com

JIHANIAN, LEVON Pg. 219
Love guides her, protects her, and consumes her. Compassion is her sword. Mercy is her torch.

www.levonjihanian.com @ForkFrenzy forkfrenzy.tumblr.com

KIKI JENKINS Pg. 142-143
What makes a Knight? Knights were created to protect something, or someone. Being a Knight means having strength, be it physical, mental, spiritual. Strength comes in many forms, and I think every single one of us, whether we realize it or not, are a Knight in our own way. We all have strength in us somewhere, even if we don't see it.

www.kikijenkinsart.com @kikaisaigono kikistiel.tumblr.com

KIM, POLYNA Pg. 139
Strength is when you finally open that pickle jar on the first try after years of failed attempts.

www.polynakim.com @milkdoggie milkdoggie.tumblr.com

KIM, YOUNG Pg. 244
For me, strength is adaptability.

www.youngkimart.com

KIMIATEK, SASHA

If we have the intention to give effort and love, we are rewarded with well-being. Strength is rekindling and protecting the light within ourselves when the world extinguishes it; even when we are left to fumble in the dark for some time.

www.sashakimiatek.com   instagram.com/sasha.kimia   @sashakimia

KINDRED, CHRIS

Strength is knowing when to heal yourself, in spite of those that won't approve of the actions needed.

chriskindred.com   @ itskindred

KIRBY, MARTIN

"A knight, to me, is duality. For all their strength, there is discipline. For all their courage, there is humility. For all their kindness, there is the overwhelming desire to battle against evil wherever it may be found. These conflicting facets are what makes a knight so powerful, and so admirable and is what makes them, in my eyes, so captivating."

kirbish.artstation.com   @kirbishart   kirbish.tumblr.com

KOTAKI, KEKAI

A character's strength comes from their weakness. The realization of what it is and the perseverance in overcoming it. And finally an acceptance of it.

www.kekaiart.com   @KekaiKotaki   kekai-k.tumblr.com

KURILICH, CAITLYN

Find strength in reflection. Those who look unblinkingly are sometimes the bravest.

www.caitlynkurilich.com   @caitlynkurilich   caitlynkurilich.tumblr.com

LAVEY-HEATON, MEGAN

Strength means having the fortitude to do the unimaginable and the wisdom to allow yourself to mourn the consequences of those actions.

www.namesakecomic.com   @savvyliterate

LEE, JACQUES

A knight is an individual who adds goodness to the world, rather than evil. To me, they will protect a wealthy lord with the same determination and resolve as they do protecting smallest mouse.

www.jacqueslee.com   @matchallama

LETENDRE, KYLE

The strongest figures in my life have always been women. They're irreverent, nurturing, and get shit done. May I be even half as selfless and patient as my mother one day.

www.kyleletendre.com   @heykylehey   heykyle.tumblr.com

LI, ALICE MEICHI

Growing up in a Chinese immigrant household where my family put aside their desires to provide a stable life to me and my sister, the strength to do what needs to be done was ingrained in me from an early age. As a result, I took my familial influences and wanted to create an image that encapsulated that value. My knight, the Rabbit on the Moon, takes no pleasure in fighting the dragon, Eclipse. She's doing it because no one else will.

www.alicemeichi.com   @alicemeichi   alicemeichi.tumblr.com

LIV, JENN

Strength comes from knowing the truest form of yourself and remaining unswayed by the distractions or fake appearances of others. Actions and good deeds speak volumes over those who only know how to put up a facade.

www.jennliv.com   @chemicalcolour   jennliv.tumblr.com

MACKENZIE, ASHLEY Pg. 26

I think there's strength in introspection, knowing yourself enough to recognize your own flaws and strengths, learning your own limitations and finding new ways to work within them or even circumvent them. All too often we're our own worst enemies.

www.ashmackenzie.com @_ashmackenzie ashmackenzie.tumblr.com

MCKEON, JENNY Pg. 145-147

My peers are my biggest inspiration—forging ahead, making new paths and new spaces for themselves and others, chasing their dreams. They really are like knights, and I strive to be one too. Our bravery, creativity, and passion will be our weapons and our armor!

www.jlmkart.com @jlmkart jlmkart.tumblr.com

MIOTKE, MEREDITH Pg. 112-113

Strength is confronting the things that scare you, then working and persisting through them.

www.mlmiotke.com @mlmiotke meredithmiotke.tumblr.com

MISTRY, BEENA Pg. 78-79

True strength is overcoming your full gut by eating all the sushi you ordered at the All-You-Can-Eat sushi place to avoid the extra charges.

www.beenamistry.com @beenathemistry beenamistryart.tumblr.com

MOUSAVI, CAMERON Pg. 10

Strength is in always trying to press forward, with or without a compass.

www.cameronmousavi.com sprias.tumblr.com

MUTCH, KEVIN Pg. 168-182

Strength to me, above all, means the ability to keep going when the entire universe is trying to kill you. Which it is.

www.kevinmutch.blogspot.com

NEWTON, MERIDEL Pg. 114-131

Don't let anything hold you back. You determine the shape of your life. Every moment is a decision—decide to be valiant.

www.thepuppetkingdom.com @ridelee

NICHOLSON, CAMERON Pg. 86

Strength isn't measured by physical Strength, It's more about the care inside.

www.westonart.format.com @prof_weston profweston.tumblr.com

NIKA Pg. 151-165

If you want to be a knight, you've got to stand for something--and that means you've got to listen to your heart. It's not going to be easy. At times, it may seem impossible. But for your efforts, you'll have gained something invaluable: the power to fight off dragons and vanquish your demons.

www.nikacomics.com @onelemonylime nikaworks.tumblr.com

NORTH, RYAN Pg. 226-230

I see strength in a character as the ability to work towards a goal. Not even achieving their goals, necessarily, but deciding to do something and then trying to do it is the tricky part, especially when the goal isn't an easy one—when there's all the reason in the world NOT to expect to achieve that goal—but then deciding to try anyway. Strength! Also it helps if they have super powers, that's powerful too.

www.qwantz.com @ryanqnorth ryannorth.tumblr.com

PARBERRY, LIZZIE Pg. 45, 217
True strength is walking past a bookstore without going in.
www.thunderbirdcomic.com   @linken_log   linkenlog.tumblr.com

PENG, LEONARD Pg. 166-167
Strength is believing in yourself and trusting your instinct.
www.leonardpeng.com   @pengtagram   pengtagram.tumblr.com

PITEIRA, ELEONOR Pg. 183
A Knight is a person of strength, and strength can be found in many forms. There is strength in enduring something and there is strength in facing the unknown, both are worthy of respect.
www.eleonorpiteira.carbonmade.com   @_eleonorp   eleonorpiteira.tumblr.com

POIRIER, PHILIPPE Pg. 93, 144, 216
There are various stages in the lives of Knights. While Hazel is a proud accomplished knight, Mirella is on her way to be knighted for writing a compendium of all the kingdom's plants. Anna and Clara are just setting out on their adventure. A knight is someone who is passionate about their craft, who values fellowship and betterment of oneself through discipline, knowledge and valor.
www.philippepoirier.ca   @philippep0irier   philippepoirierart.tumblr.com

PRIMARY HUGHES Pg. 91
Resiliency.
www.primaryhughes.com   @primaryhughes   primaryhughes.tumblr.com

PULIDO, LIZ Pg. 224
"Strength" isn't a physical trait to me — it's your willingness to fail and fail gloriously with every ounce of effort you have over and over again to achieve your dreams. There's a tendency to associate strength with perfection or how effortlessly a challenge is overcome. But the strongest characters and the people I admire most? Their strength lies in their tenacity; their willingness to confront their weaknesses and fears without hesitation.
www.lizpulido.com   lizsketch.tumblr.com   instagram/lizsketch

ROCKEFELLER, MATT Pg. 14-15
A strong character pursues their goals and dreams despite the people, forces, and constructs that work against them. However, they are able to concede this strength when they come across another worthy path or point of view. With the ability to adapt and a willingness to see the world from another perspective, a strong character is both passionate and compassionate!
www.mattrockefeller.com   @mcrockefeller   mrockefeller.tumblr.com

ROUX, JESSICA Pg. 148-149
I find strength (and inspiration!) in nature. Nature is not only a beautiful muse for the flora and fauna often found in my work; nature is also strong, dangerous and honest—just like a knight.
www.jessica-roux.com   @jessicasroux   jessicaroux.tumblr.com

SATONE, VANESSA Pg. 46-51
I believe strength is the ability to stand up for what you believe in, or doing the right thing even if you may suffer consequences.
www.visforvacant.com   @vsatone   vsatone.tumblr.com

SCHULTZ, MIKE Pg. 73
I think that being a knight and a warrior is only partly about fighting the good fight. It is also about one's deliberate approach to each situation, and how you handle yourself and treat others during times of great adversity. To me, that is true strength!
www.mikeschultzstudio.com   @mike_schultz_studio   instagram.com/mike_schultz_studio

SCIORTINO, FLEUR Pg. 13, 234
A knight is someone with flaws, but despite their limitations and setbacks, they still find ways to overcome them - especially when concerned with helping others. Whether it's a brave knight fending off dangerous attackers, or a friend who'll go out of their way to help you when you need it most.

@fleurtater   fleursciortino.tumblr.com   fleurdraws.tumblr.com   instagram.com/fleursciortino

SIX, SAÏNA Pg. 92
To me, strength means embracing and acknowledging your fears and weaknesses but being able get back on your feet as many times as needed and never give up.

www.sainasix.com   instagram.com/sainasix   @sainasix

SMITH, JENNIFER ZYREN Pg. 208-214
We generally think of knights as fighters and I think in part that's true. The fighting doesn't need to be with traditional weapons; it can be with the heart or mind. A knight is someone willing to stand up for what's right, no matter what they stand to lose, and no matter how scared they are.

www.lasalleslegacy.com   @jenniferzyren   zyrenskistudios.tumblr.com

SMITH, KELLY Pg. 12
True strength is having the courage to be kind and stand up for others; even when it is easier not to.

@beatfist   beatfist.tumblr.com

SOLEAS, JOHN Pg. 223
Strength is being able to bench press a moose while simultaneously fighting for what you believe in.

www.johnsoleas.ca   yiannisun.tumblr.com

STANTON, KEVIN JAY Pg 226-230
I think strength is the shortcut between knowing what is right and doing it.

www.kevinjaystanton.com   @kevinjaystanton   kevinjaystanton.tumblr.com

STOCKTON, KAT Pg 240
When I think of strength, I think of the bonds between families, neighbors, and friends. I think of the times we've supported each other through the good and the bad and our perseverance. Real strength is tied to love in some ambiguous way and when you love someone your giving them strength.

www.katstockton.com   @katstocktonart   katstockton.tumblr.com

SUGAR, STEVEN Pg. 200-201
Strength can't just be found- it has to be made! Strength has to be built bit by bit, grown with determination and courage!

@stesug   stevensugar.tumblr.com

SUNG, JANET Pg. 232
"Training is useful but there is no substitute for experience." —Lotte Lenya

www.janetsungart.com   @kuru731   janetsungart.tumblr.com

TALMADGE, SARA Pg. 136
A knight is anything you want it to be, as long as it taps into your own unique strength and ferocity. As a knight you can never be dressed "too sexy" or "too modest", "too girly" or "too mannish", because you are dressed the way you feel strongest and most confident, the way you feel inside. Armor, mech suit, bikini, or anything else is appropriate attire for a knight if it is the attire she chooses. There is simply no wrong way to be a knight if you live and fight for your passion.

www.saratalmadge.com   @charapoo   charapoo.tumblr.com

TIERNEY, JOSH   Pg. 198-199
Strength is having the courage to protect those you love.

@jwtierney   joshtierney.tumblr.com

TONG, ANGELA   Pg. 243, 245
I think that a knight is somebody who believes in fighting for good, whatever their view of good might be. And that's not necessarily just fighting in battles with big swords... it's also quietly making people feel good about themselves or struggling to remain positive everyday. Fighting for what you believe in and spreading joy.

@lukeanderin   angelatong.tumblr.com

TYTO-ALBA   Pg. 192
A strong character comes in the form of heart and dedication to one's craft. They are defined not by appearance, but by the will of their being. Hindered not by the challenges they face, no matter how big or small, physical or mental. It is their will to overcome, and prove one's self. Even if they do not succeed, it is their determination to try, and try again that will prove themselves strong.

ttyto-alba.tumblr.com   @_tyto_alba   instagram.com/_tyto_alba

VIDAURRI, S.M.   Pg 62 -69
Being strong is often seen as being synonymous with victory, but there is also a lot of strength in losing. Even if it costs you down the line, choosing to adhere to your principles and not letting yourself be taken advantage of.

www.smvidaurri.co   @smvidaurri   smvidaurri.tumblr.com

VIGANTS, JUDE   Pg. 185-191
Strength, even in a physical/emotional/mental sense, comes from being resilient. I believe that true strength at it's core comes from love. The strongest heroes, and villains, are or at once were, standing up for what the love and what they feel they need to fight for. Strength rooted in fear will crumble. Strength rooted in hate is no strength at all. Strength rooted in love is the real deal.

www.junevigants.com   @junerevolver   junerevolver.tumblr.com

WEGENER, SCOTT   Pg. 41
Trying to define strength is really hard. I think the best definition I can come up with is that true inner strength develops from an honest understanding of ourselves. When you can see yourself for who and what you really are, the good and the bad, it becomes very difficult for outside force to rattle you.

www.atomic-robo.com   @scott_wegna

WILDING, IAN   Pg. 150
A knight wears a suit of armor whilst engaging with fire-breathing machines.

www.iwilding.com   @iwilding   iwilding.tumblr.com

WISHBOW, PAM   Pg. 242, 246-247
Strength to me is knowing when or not to use the power you have. Be it physical, emotional, spiritual, whatever. It's easy to have power, it's hard to know when to use it. Strength is when you know when to fight. A strong warrior doesn't get into fights left and right, that's a bully. An leader doesn't spin stories, that's a liar. They fight, they tell tales to evoke something but it's not something you throw around. Strength is getting that power and really knowing when and how to wield it.

www.pamwishbow.com   @pamwishbow   wishbow.tumblr.com

WOODALL, JENN   Pg. 236-237
Strength is the ability to persevere tough situations and to possess the resistance to not let it tear you down.

www.jennwoodall.format.com   @jenn_woodall   jwoodall.tumblr.com

WRIGHT, GREG   Pg. 241
Big or small, good or bad, a knight is the sword and shield that protects another.

@goldcucco   greg-wright.tumblr.com

WRIGHT, SHANNON Pg. 134

You can find your strength in wanting to protect or provide for those dearest to you. Inspiration can come from being able to relate to a person and that's one reason representation matters; it inspires those who don't normally see themselves being portrayed and allows them to say, "I can be all those things society tells me I'm not meant to be.

www.shannon-wright.com @shannondrewthis shannondrewthis.tumblr.com

XU, RU Pg. 137, 248

Adversity tests a character's mettle, but it's their humanizing actions —both small and grand—that makes a character for me! It's a hint at a rich backstory that the reader is invited to create.

www.saintforrent.com @ruemxu ruemxu.tumblr.com

YEE, REIMENA Pg. 36

To be able to let go and yet preserve yourself.

www.reimenayee.com @reimenayee reimenaashelyee.tumblr.com

YING, JONATHAN Pg. 18-23

Strength is often either how effectively a character can push against his or her surroundings, or it's the character's resilience when those same surroundings push back. Context is key; you can never know the true strength of a character until they are faced with a meaningful challenge.

www.jonathanying.com @fancymancer

YING, VICTORIA Pg. 18-23

What makes a character strong? Conviction. The ability to do what they think is right even though it's hard.

www.victoriaying.com @victoriaying

ZABRZESKA, ZOFIA Pg. 24-25, 215, 235

It's not the armor that creates a knight but a cause. Despite obstacles, bravely and selflessly they fight for and protect what they believe in.

www.zofiazabrzeska.wixsite.com/portfolio pan-sowa.tumblr.com

Dear Reader,

Thank you for picking up this book. There are 1001 characters over the course of three volumes that make up 1001 Knights. The book in your hands is the third — **WISDOM**. Every artist and Kickstarter backer are knights and now by finishing this book, you are a part of this dialogue too.

Art can change us and inspire us to do great things. Now that you have read these stories, you can go forth and make the world a better place. Share this book, support and check out the 1001 Knights artists. You are always welcome in the 1001 Knights community.

RISE A KNIGHT.

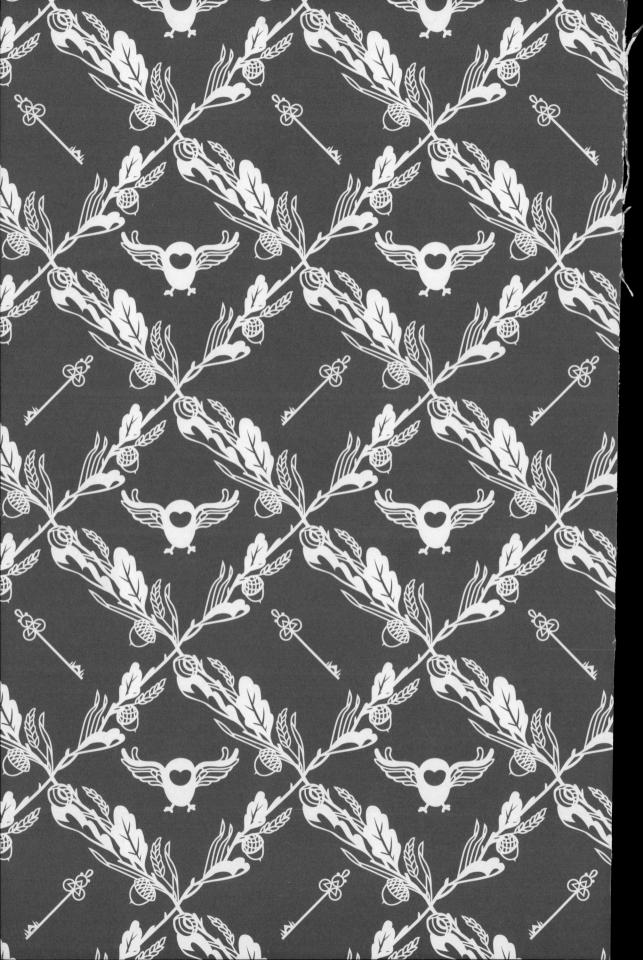